Freddie Fireflies

AND THE SACRAMENTS

FR TIM'S TALES FOR CHRISTIAN CHILDREN

Enjoy

Fr Tim

A Redemptorist Publication

Published by **Redemptorist Publications**

Alphonsus House, Chawton, Hampshire, GU34 3HQ, UK
Tel. +44 (0)1420 88222, Fax. +44 (0)1420 88805
Email rp@rpbooks.co.uk, www.rpbooks.co.uk

A registered charity limited by guarantee
Registered in England 3261721

Text copyright © Timothy J. Buckley C.Ss.R., 2014
Illustrations copyright © Redemptorist Publications 2014
First published November 2014

Text by Timothy J. Buckley C.Ss.R.
Edited by Rachel Thompson
Designed by Nuttifox
Illustrated by Jane Morgan

ISBN 978-0-85231-418-0

A CIP catalogue record for this book is available from the British Library.

The publisher gratefully acknowledges permission to use the excerpts from THE
JERUSALEM BIBLE, copyright © 1966 by Darton, Longman & Todd, Ltd and
Doubleday, a division of Random House, Inc. Reprinted by permission. Scripture
quoted from the GOOD NEWS BIBLE © 1994 is published by the Bible Societies/
HarperCollins Publishers Ltd UK, Good News Bible © American Bible Society 1966,
1971, 1976, 1992. Used with permission.

Printed by Portland Print, Kettering, NN16 8UN

Introduction

Freddie and the Sacraments

Since publishing the first book of "Freddie Freckles" stories, I have been working as a parish priest in two sizeable parishes on the south side of Liverpool, each with a large primary school of over four hundred children. In recent years the Archdiocese of Liverpool has introduced a Family Catechesis programme for all the sacraments, and children in Year Four are now prepared through the parishes for the sacraments of Reconciliation, Confirmation and first Holy Communion. They receive their first Holy Communion at the Mass of Confirmation. The programme is an ambitious one, designed to involve the parents throughout the process, recognising that they are the first teachers of their children in the ways of faith.

I have sought to encourage both parents and children in the parishes of Our Lady of the Annunciation (commonly known as Bishop Eton) and St Mary's Woolton, by supplementing the material in their handbooks with a series of stories, designed to highlight the main points they have been covering at each stage. I have also added some of my own insights, which hopefully will prove helpful. It is my hope that these stories will be of use to all those involved in these sacramental programmes in the Liverpool Archdiocese. Indeed, I hope they will prove useful to all young children and their parents and catechists preparing for the sacraments of Reconciliation, Confirmation and first Holy Communion.

The stories were written with a view to me telling them to the groups of children in the sacramental programme. I then made them available to each child so that they could read them for themselves. I would anticipate that this would be the ideal way in which to use them; that is, firstly narrating them to a group of children and inviting their participation where appropriate and then encouraging them to read the stories for themselves.

Timothy J. Buckley C.Ss.R.

Contents

COME TO THE WATER

Come to the Water

The lesson
The purpose of the story is to put children in touch with their Baptism and help them to be familiar with a main features in a church building.

Scripture references
> *As Jesus was coming up out of the water the Spirit came down upon him and a voice from heaven said, "You are my Son, whom I love."* (Mark 1:9-11)

> *Go, therefore, make disciples of all the nations; baptise them in the name of the Father and of the Son and of the Holy Spirit... And know that I am with you always; yes, to the end of time.* (Matthew 28:19-20)

When to tell this story
This story is designed to help children when they begin to prepare for the sacraments of initiation, which include Confirmation and Holy Communion. Helping children to understand what happened for them at their Baptism will enable them to prepare for their Confirmation, when they will make their baptismal promises for themselves. The story is also designed to ensure that they are familiar with all the important features in the church, including the altar, on which the Eucharist is celebrated, and the lectern, from which the Gospel is proclaimed.

Note
With you always is the title of the sacramental programme in Liverpool and, of course, they are the words which end St Matthew's Gospel, when Jesus sends his disciples out to baptise people all over the world.

COME TO THE WATER

Freddie Freckles was really excited. It was the beginning of a new school year and he was now going into Year Four, which meant that he would be in the class preparing for Confirmation and first Holy Communion.

For years Freddie had been going to church and seeing his mum and dad and then his older sister, Suzie, go up to receive Holy Communion. He knew it was very special because everyone went up the aisle of the church with their hands joined and their heads bowed. It was obvious that they were praying very hard. When he was very little he used to ask his mum and dad why he couldn't have what they were having. They would simply tell him that when he was bigger he would be able to learn all about what Jesus had promised us. Meanwhile the priest would say a special prayer over him if he came up with them. So, Freddie had learnt to come up the aisle with his head bowed and his arms across his chest and the priest would say the prayer over him. He liked that and he always smiled at the priest, who smiled back.

Now the time had come when he was old enough to start learning all about the wonderful things Jesus had done for his disciples and the promises he had made to them. Freddie couldn't wait for the first meeting, which was going to be in the church one Sunday afternoon. All the mums and dads and children were there on time and the team of special teachers, called catechists, were ready to explain to them what was going to happen. Freddie was really pleased when he realised that he would be working with his mum and dad on all the subjects they were going to explore. That afternoon they had a fabulous time looking at many of the different things that are in the church.

When the group arrived they were asked to pay special attention to the holy water stoop near the door. Although Freddie had made the sign of the cross on himself loads of times before, he had never realised that when he did it entering the church with the holy water on the tip of his finger it was to remind him of his Baptism. Freddie was only a tiny baby when he was baptised and the priest had poured water over his head. One of the catechists told the group that they would end the session thinking about Baptism.

But for now they were being sent on a treasure hunt. Armed with worksheets all the boys and girls and their parents started moving round the church, checking everything on the list. Freddie was able to tick off most of the items easily. He saw the crucifix which showed Jesus dying on the cross for us and then he saw the Easter candle. The light was flickering and Freddie knew it stood for Jesus, risen from the dead. He saw the tabernacle, the little house behind the altar where Holy Communion is kept and the lamp that burns nearby to remind us that Jesus is always present there. When Holy Communion is kept in the tabernacle it is called the Blessed Sacrament and Freddie knew that the word "sacrament" was one he needed to understand. A sacrament is a sign of God's presence and he was being prepared to receive three of them in the next few months. Freddie saw the holy oils, which the bishop had blessed in the cathedral just before Easter and he knew that he would be anointed with one of those oils at the sacrament of Confirmation.

Freddie took his turn carrying the gifts of bread and wine up the aisle, something he had done for real on some Sundays when it had been his family's turn to help. He stood by the altar and saw the Missal which has all the prayers of the Mass in it. Freddie knew the altar was really important: it is in the centre of the holy part of the church called the sanctuary and it reminds us of how Jesus gathered his friends around a table for that Last Supper before he died. Freddie looked at the lectern, the place from which all the readings are done and reminded himself that he had heard lots of interesting messages about how to live well, both from the readings and what the priest had said to explain them. Of course he wasn't able to understand everything, but as he was growing older he realised that he was beginning to understand more and more. His priest was really good at telling the children stories and Freddie was starting to make all sorts of connections.

What really got Freddie excited at this first meeting, however, and what led to him make loads of connections, was when he went to look at the Baptism Register. Inside this book he saw his name: **FREDERICK FRANCIS FRECKLES**, with the date of his birth and the date of his Baptism, and underneath were the names of his parents and his godparents. Freddie knew his godmother very well; she was his Aunty Margaret and she always remembered to keep in touch and remind him that she had a special job to do, helping his mum and dad look after him. Sadly his godfather had died when Freddie was very young. He knew that his godfather was his Uncle James and that he had been very brave, going to the help of a little boy who was in danger of drowning in the river. Uncle James had dived into the freezing cold water and saved the little boy, but afterwards he was taken ill and he died. Freddie's dad used this occasion to remind him that his godfather had done what Jesus said was the greatest thing anyone could do: he had given his life to save someone else. And of course his dad reminded him that this was what Jesus was doing when he was on the cross, saving us all from the bad things and the sins that people commit. "Freddie," he said, "that was why your mum and I and Aunty Margaret and Uncle James made the sign of the cross on your forehead at the beginning of your baptism service. With the priest we were saying that we want Freddie to be protected by this wonderful God who sent his son, Jesus, into our world. Then we all made an act of faith in God for you. Soon you will be making that act of faith for yourself when you are confirmed. The priest then poured the water over your head and said, 'Frederick Francis, I baptise you in the name of the Father and of the Son and of the Holy Spirit.'"

Freddie's dad had to stop talking at that moment because everyone was being called around the Easter candle. Candles were handed to those children who didn't have their own baptism candles. Freddie's parents had been careful to look after his candle which was kept on a special table in his bedroom and they had brought it with them today. Now, as all the candles were being lit from the Easter candle, the children were reminded that on their baptism day a candle had been given to their parents and godparents with the command that this symbolic light was to be kept burning brightly. Of course the symbol was that the light of Jesus – who had said he was the light of the world – would light up their lives so that other people could see what it means to be a friend of Jesus. As all the parents watched their children with their candles they felt very proud of them and of the fact that they had kept the promises they had made to bring up their children to know and love Jesus.

When they returned home that evening Freddie asked his parents all sorts of questions. He wanted to know more about his family and his godparents' families going back over the years. He had seen part of a programme on television called "Who do you think you are?" in which a famous person was finding out about his ancestors and all the amazing things they had done. Freddie began to realise that some of his ancestors had done amazing things too and that it was because of them all that he is who he is today. He had never thought about it like that before, but it also helped him understand this business of handing on from one generation to another is the way it works in the Church too. Jesus had told his disciples that they must be "the light of the world" and that handing on the light was just what they had been doing at their little ceremony at the end of the afternoon.

As Freddie went to bed that night he prayed a "thank you" prayer for all the people who had loved and cared for him during his life and all the people who were now making sure that he knew he was also a child of God. He couldn't wait for the next session when he would be thinking about the importance of names.

CALLED BY NAME

Called by Name

The lesson

This story is designed to highlight the importance and significance of names and the fact that God knows our names and calls us to be his friends and followers.

Scripture references

Simon's name is changed to Peter (which means "rock") after he says he knows that Jesus is the Christ.

> *Jesus replied, "Simon, son of Jonah, you are a happy man! Because it was not flesh and blood that revealed this to you but my Father in heaven. So I now say to you: You are Peter and on this rock I will build my Church."*
>
> (Matthew 16:17-18)

Likewise Abram is to be called Abraham (which means "father of a multitude").

> *God said to him: "You shall no longer to be called Abram; your name shall be Abraham, for I make you father of a multitude of nations."*
>
> (Genesis 17:5)

When to tell this story

This story could be told to children at any time to remind them of how precious they are in the sight of God. It will carry a special significance when children are trying to determine a confirmation name. When this is the case it is important to encourage the children to choose a name which will be significant and inspiring for them. Researching the name and the people associated with it (saint or family member) can be a very rewarding exercise. They might choose one of their baptismal names and learn more about why they were baptised with that name.

CALLED BY NAME

Freddie Freckles arrived for the second session of the sacramental programme really keen to learn more about the importance of names. You will remember that after the first session he had begun to get really interested in his family and especially in his Uncle James, his godfather who had sadly died before he could get to know him. However, because he had died as a brave man, saving someone else's life, Freddie felt close to him. He realised that his Uncle James was very close to Jesus because he had done the very thing that Jesus had said was the greatest sign of a person's love.

All the children began by talking with their parents about their own names and why they were called those names. Later, when they did some sharing in the group, they realised that there were all sorts of reasons why people had different names. Some children were called after their parents or even grandparents or great grandparents, but many had been given new names which their parents liked for a particular reason. Freddie discovered that his great granddad had been called Frederick and he held a special place in the family history because he was deaf and had spent his life teaching sign language to others who were deaf. Freddie also discovered something else: St Frederick is the patron saint of people who are deaf. There was a little girl in his class, Lucy, who had trouble hearing and Freddie suddenly felt a new connection with her and they were to become special friends.

The group began to think about how important names were in the stories in the scriptures. Before Jesus came into the world we have the story of his people, the Jewish people, in what we call the Old Testament. Sometimes names were changed because of the special jobs people were given. "Abram", which means "exalted father" was changed to "Abraham", which means "father of a multitude" and Abraham was to become the father of the whole Jewish nation. In the New Testament we have the stories about Jesus in the Gospels, and in the other books and letters we hear about his friends and the early Christians. In these books too we learn a lot about names.

Firstly the children were reminded that the name "Jesus" is a very holy name because it actually means "Saviour" and of course is a name that should never be used for swearing. Then they realised that Jesus actually changed the first Pope's name. When Jesus called him and his brother, Andrew, from their work as fishermen, his name was Simon. Jesus changed Simon's name to Peter, a name which means "rock", because he needed to be the strong foundation on which the whole Church was going to be built. At this point in the session the group stopped to think about how Jesus called all his friends to be his followers. Jesus always called them by name and the children began to understand that this was exactly the meaning of their naming at Baptism. It was truly important: like the first disciples they were being called personally by Jesus to be his friends and to spread his message of love and hope and forgiveness.

Freddie's ears had pricked up when he heard about Peter getting his new name because his second baptismal name was Francis and the new Pope had taken the name Francis after he had been elected. They had been talking about St Francis in class at school and Freddie found himself liking this man who had lived eight hundred years ago and had caused a great stir by saying that he didn't want to be rich, but wanted to live close to the poor people who needed his love and his prayers. The Pope had taken his name because he wanted everyone in the Church to think in the same way and Freddie liked the idea of helping people who were poor or unhappy. He realised that he had been lucky, having a good mum and dad and lots of things which make life enjoyable and he knew that many other children were not so lucky.

Freddie had been thinking about the name he must choose for the sacrament of Confirmation and he asked his mum and dad if he could choose Francis. His mum and dad weren't sure whether he had to choose a new name and as Fr Tim had turned up to the session they went over and asked him. Fr Tim then made a big announcement and explained to everyone that when choosing a Confirmation name the important thing is to choose a name which has meaning for you because it is someone who will inspire you and to whom you can pray. "Therefore," he said, "it is perfectly in order either to choose a new name or to choose one of your baptismal names (if you share a saint's name). Just make sure that you do all you can to find out as much as you can about the saint and then he or she can become one of your special friends in heaven."

Before we end this story, you need to know that Freddie was worried about something. There were twins in the group, Angela and Anthony, and Freddie knew there was something troubling them. Their dad was in the army and was away a lot of the time and their mum hadn't been well, so it was sometimes difficult for them to get to the meetings or to get to Mass on a Sunday. The catechists and Fr Tim had explained that it was important to come to all the sessions and since they would soon be receiving Holy Communion for the first time, it was important to get into the habit of coming to Mass regularly. And there was a further problem: Anthony was a really good footballer and played for one of the local teams and the matches were usually on a Sunday morning. Thinking about how St Francis was a saint who was on the lookout for people with problems, Freddie decided to tell his mum and dad about the situation. His mum was really thoughtful and sensible and she decided to have a quiet word with Angela and Anthony's mum. The outcome was just brilliant. Angela and Anthony's mum was really grateful that Mrs Freckles had raised the subject and said she had been worrying about what to do. Without further ado it was agreed that the Freckles family would check each week how she was and if necessary they would pick up Angela and Anthony on their way to Mass or to the group sessions. As Anthony began to feel more part of the group he began to worry less about missing the odd football match, not least because he realised that Freddie had made a big sacrifice by changing his football club when he saw the times were going to clash. In any case there were Masses at different times in different churches which they could go to and on a couple of occasions they all went to Mass on the Saturday or Sunday evening.

The next session was going to be about the sacrament of Reconciliation. "Reconciliation" is a big word which means "making peace" and includes saying "sorry" when we have offended or upset others. Already there were lots of questions rising up in Freddie's mind, but they could wait. He went to bed that night, peaceful in the knowledge that he had done some good and helpful things like his patron, St Francis.

I AM SORRY

I am Sorry

The lesson
The story is written to help children reflect on the importance of learning to apologise when we misbehave. It is written positively to show children that when we make up, our friendships actually become stronger. Our reason for saying "sorry" to Jesus is because he told us that whatever we do to one another we do to him.

Scripture references
Jesus reminded his listeners that when they looked after other people who were hungry or thirsty or sick or in any kind of trouble, they were actually looking after him, because we are all his brothers and sisters.
> *I tell you solemnly, in so far as you did this to one of the least of these brothers or sisters of mine, you did it to me.* (Matthew 25:40)

We must never stop forgiving one another. When Peter asked Jesus how often he should forgive; would seven times be enough?
> *Jesus answered: "Not seven, I tell you, but seventy-seven times."* (Matthew 18:22)

St Paul reminded us that God can turn everything to good.
> *We know that by turning everything to their good God co-operates with all those who love him.* (Romans 8.28)

When to tell this story
This is a story which would fit any occasion when seeking to teach children to be forgiving. It has special significance for those preparing for the celebration of the sacrament of Reconciliation.

Note
This is a story which lends itself to group participation, checking with the children as to whether they can recall similar experiences.

I AM SORRY

Freddie Freckles had gone to school one morning and he was feeling very grumpy. At breakfast his sister, Suzie, had spilt the milk all over the table and had tried to blame Freddie, saying he had pushed her in the back. Well he had, but he was only trying to be playful and friendly. In the end both Freddie and his sister had been in trouble with their mum and dad. Then, when Freddie arrived at school his teacher told him off for messing around after the bell had gone because the children were supposed to be lining up in silence to go into their classrooms. So now he felt even more grumpy and miserable and thought the whole world was against him.

When it came to playtime Freddie was still feeling miserable. Instead of joining in the football as usual he decided to be a nuisance and start spoiling everyone else's fun. He ran across the playground, deliberately interfering with other people's games. He kicked a couple of balls over the wall into a garden and he bumped into a few boys and girls, pretending he hadn't noticed them. Eventually the teacher on duty saw what was happening and called Freddie over and he was told to go and sit quietly outside the head teacher's office. While he was sitting there Freddie had time to calm down and think things over. He began to feel very sad and sorry for himself. He said to himself in his mind, "Why am I in such a bad mood and behaving so badly? I really don't understand myself."

The head teacher, Mr James, came and sat down to have a chat with Freddie about what had been going on. Freddie was honest and told him the whole story, going right back to breakfast time. Mr James was a very wise man and he did not get angry with Freddie. In fact he quickly had Freddie smiling and laughing at himself. You see, Freddie had told Mr James that, although he was fed up, he couldn't understand why he had become so angry. Mr James said, "Freddie, you remind me of St Paul." Then he went on to tell him about St Paul's letter to his friends in Rome, where St Paul says exactly what Freddie had said: "I cannot understand my own behaviour: when I want to do good things, I end up doing bad things." Mr James told Freddie that St Paul eventually worked it out and realised that he needed God to help him to do the right thing, especially when he didn't feel on good form. St Paul learnt to say sorry to God and to the people he had upset and spent the rest of his life teaching people to ask Jesus to help them to live good lives, just the way God the Father wants. Freddie now began to feel much better about things and about himself and he went back to his class with a smile on his face.

Mr James asked Freddie to be sure to say "sorry" to all the people he had upset. When he went into the room he apologised to his teacher and the children whose games he had messed up. At lunchtime he got permission to go round to the house with the garden where the balls had landed when he had kicked them over the wall earlier. Freddie's friend, Peter Pickles went with him and made it easier for him by doing the talking to begin with, though Freddie did say he was sorry for the trouble he had caused to the old man who owned the house. The old man said they were not to worry and went out into the garden to find the balls, telling the two boys that they were very polite.

When Freddie went home that evening, his mum and dad were quick to say "sorry" to both Suzie and Freddie for getting so angry with them over what was really quite a small matter. In fact his dad was on good form and started joking about how silly it is to "cry over spilt milk" and the danger of causing "a storm in a teacup", which was obviously a reference to the fact that his teacup had been knocked over in the confusion as well. This caused Suzie to laugh and she apologised to Freddie for blaming him: she knew he had only been playful and had not meant to cause the accident. But now Freddie was willing to accept his responsibility and he said to Suzie, "No, in fairness I realise that I made you jump which led to the spilling of the milk." Mrs Freckles said she had been worried about all the things she had got to do that day and knew that she had been too quick to get angry. All this got Freddie thinking again. He began to work out that in a strange way all the trouble in the morning had led everyone in the family to be especially kind and forgiving that evening.

At bedtime, Freddie's dad said, "I think we should use the holy water tonight, Freddie." All the children in the sacramental programme class had received a small bottle of holy water. The idea was that they would bless their parents with it and in turn the parents would bless them. Freddie and his dad blessed one another with the holy water and his dad began to chat to him about the events of the day. Freddie told him what had happened at school and how Mr James had spoken to him about St Paul also getting grumpy. Freddie's dad said, "I'll tell you something else about St Paul. In that same letter to the Romans he also said that God can turn everything to good, and that is exactly what has happened today. We had a bad start to the day, but in the end we were all big enough to say 'sorry' to one another and now we are a happier and more united family than ever."

Freddie's dad went on to remind him that very soon he would be receiving the sacrament of Reconciliation for the first time. "Reconciliation" is a big word which just means "making up" or "making peace". "But Daddy," said Freddie, "why do I have to go and tell God I am sorry if I have already made up and made peace with everyone I upset?" "Ah," said his dad, "that is a really good question. Freddie, do you remember when Jesus was teaching his disciples about looking after people, he said, 'Whatever you do to one of the least of these people, you do to me.' We have just used the holy water, which reminds us that because of our Baptism we are filled with the life of God. And when you receive Holy Communion in a few months' time you will be further reminded that Jesus is living within you. So, Freddie, if he is living in you, he is also living in Suzie and Mum, Peter Pickles and all your friends and me. That's why we need to say 'sorry' to Jesus as well." Freddie said he understood, but still wondered why he needed to go and talk to the priest about it. His dad went on to explain that when Jesus came back after his resurrection and met the apostles, he forgave them for all the things they had done wrong, like being cowards and running away when he needed them. And then he told the apostles to go and forgive other people in his name. Jesus was helping them to understand that we all make one big family in the Church and that our sins do spoil the friendship and unity of the big family. So the priest is there on behalf of the family to let us know that Jesus has forgiven us and that we remain united and friends, just as we have experienced in our own little family today.

Freddie had been worried about having to confess to the priest, but now that he was beginning to understand he felt much better about things. He thought to himself, "If I feel this good after we have all forgiven in our own little family, how much better will I feel when I have told God how sorry I am for my sins?" His dad had explained that when he went to see the priest Freddie would be expected to tell the priest something he was really pleased he had done because it had been good and made other people happy. This would remind him that because Jesus lives in us we do lots of good things too. Then Freddie would tell the priest what he had done wrong and how sorry he was. The priest would remind him how much Jesus loves him and say the prayer of forgiveness.

Freddie slept very well that night.

THE CHRISTMAS PLAY

The Christmas Play

The lesson
The story is designed to help children to focus on the true meaning of Christmas in the midst of all the excitement that surrounds the time of preparation, the season of Advent.

Scripture references
God loved the world so much that he gave his only Son. (John 3:16)
The Christmas story in Luke (1:26-56; 2:1-20) and Matthew (1:18–2:12)

When to tell this story
Once again, although this story is set in the midst of Freddie's period of preparation for the sacraments, it could easily be adapted and told to children of all ages in the build-up to Christmas.

THE CHRISTMAS PLAY

Freddie Freckles loved Christmas and that wonderful time of preparation called "Advent". This year he was particularly excited because the sacramental programme group was going to be involved in a "Christmas Special". The plan was not just to put it on in the church for the parishioners, but to take it to the shopping centre on the Saturday before Christmas so that all the shoppers could be reminded of the true meaning of Christmas. All the children were going to take part and Freddie didn't mind that he hadn't been chosen for one of the special parts; he was to be one of twenty shepherds. The group planned to recreate the Christmas story in a short play with music and dance and the school choir was going to take part as well. Freddie's school had a wonderful choir. In fact it was so good that the new Lord Mayor had asked that they sing in the Town Hall on the day he was to be made Lord Mayor.

All the necessary permissions were granted to put the Christmas Special on in a public place. When the Lord Mayor noticed what was happening he offered to come and say a word at the beginning. Permission had also been granted to take a collection for the children in a school which was twinned with Freddie's school. It was in a part of Africa where many people were very poor and a lot of the children were orphans. Their parents often died young because of diseases and lack of medicine. Over the years Freddie's school had raised lots of money to help these children and the "thank you" letters and photographs which the African children had sent were displayed in the school entrance.

Freddie and his friends had a great time on the third Sunday of Advent when they presented their Christmas Special in the church and now they were preparing to take it to the shopping centre. Many of the shepherds had been chosen to hold large posters during the singing of the carols. Freddie knew most of the carols off by heart, so he was able to sing and hold his poster. His poster read: GOD GAVE US THE GREATEST PRESENT OF ALL: HIS SON, JESUS. His friend, Peter Pickles, had a poster which read: MAKE AN AFRICAN CHILD HAPPY THIS CHRISTMAS – GIVE WHAT YOU CAN TO OUR SPECIAL COLLECTION. Other posters reminded the shoppers of these words in the Acts of the Apostles: THERE IS MORE HAPPINESS IN GIVING THAN RECEIVING. This poster helped Freddie remember a lesson he had learnt when he was very young. He was only in the infant class and he had received a lovely box of chocolates from his favourite Aunty Margaret. However, he had been very selfish. Freddie had taken the chocolates to school, but he had hidden them and eaten them all. In the end he had a very sore tummy and felt sad inside. The next day, Peter Pickles had arrived with a big box of sweets, which he had received from his aunty, but he shared them with all the class and everyone was really pleased and thanked Peter. Freddie noticed how happy this made Peter and he thought about how sad he had felt the day before when he had been so selfish. It was a really important lesson which he never forgot and it made him a much more generous and kind person.

Crowds and crowds of people stopped and watched the Christmas Special and joined in the carols and songs. The Lord Mayor who had spoken at the beginning stayed for the whole of the play and was seen encouraging people to stop and join in. Some of the parents accompanied the children who had collection boxes and Freddie couldn't help noticing that people were being very generous, putting in lots of money for the children in their twinned school. When all the money was counted it came to a new record for their school. This was announced at the last assembly before the Christmas holidays by Mr James, the head teacher, who congratulated all the children and their families on the wonderful effort. He told them that he had been in touch with the school in Africa and had arranged for the money to be transferred immediately to their bank. He explained that this meant that the African children would all receive a wonderful present for Christmas.

Back in class, Freddie's teacher suggested that they all write down, draw and paint how they felt about the Christmas Special and what it had meant to them. They had no trouble in doing this and it made a wonderful classroom display to end the term. There were brilliant paintings of the children in Africa as Freddie and his friends imagined them. They had remembered that they would be sitting out in the sunshine, not sitting all cosy around a fire. Most importantly, all the children wrote about how the whole experience had helped them to think about the true meaning of Christmas, a word which of course means "Christ's Mass". Many of them wrote about how it had made them feel less selfish. Instead of thinking about all the presents they wanted to receive, they had been more concerned about what they could give to help other people be happy.

The children also said they had begun to think more and more about how difficult it must have been for Mary and Joseph, having to give birth to Jesus in such difficult surroundings: a stable where they needed the breath of the animals to help keep them warm. They reflected on the fact that the visitors to the stable were reminding us that Jesus had come for everybody. He was visited by ordinary people like the shepherds. And when the wise men came from the east they were representing people from all over the world, helping us remember that Jesus had come to be a friend of all men and women in every time and place.

The session ended with a discussion about what they had painted and written and then their teacher reminded them again of the word, "Christmas". She said, "Remember, children, that you are preparing for your Confirmation and first Holy Communion. You will receive these great sacraments at your special Mass in a few months' time. Jesus was born into our world so that he could teach us about his Father's love for us. He gave us the Mass so that we can stay close to him and his Father. So have a wonderful **Christ's Mass** and remember to go to Mass on Christmas Day!"

THE GIFTS OF THE HOLY SPIRIT

The Gifts of the Holy Spirit

The lesson

Jesus promised to send the Holy Spirit to them. The Spirit's gifts would help them live their lives to the full. This is what we celebrate in the sacrament of Confirmation. The story is designed to help the children realise that new beginnings offer us wonderful opportunities. The gifts of the Holy Spirit are explained in way that will enable the children to see them as blessings to help them, not just a list to be remembered.

Scripture references

Jesus said: "The Holy Spirit, whom the Father will send in my name, will teach you everything and remind you of all I have said to you." (John 14:26)

The nearest we get to a list of the gifts of the Holy Spirit in the scriptures is to be found in the Prophet Isaiah:

A shoot springs from the stock of Jesse... on him the spirit of the Lord rests, a spirit of wisdom and insight, a spirit of counsel and power, a spirit of knowledge and of the fear of the Lord. (Isaiah 11:1-2)

When children make an act of faith, they are like Peter, who answered the question about who Jesus was, by saying:

"You are the Christ, the Son of the living God." (Matthew 16:16)

When to tell this story

This story was written specifically for those immediately preparing for the sacrament of Confirmation, but equally it could be shared with children who are facing new beginnings in life for whatever reason or as a way of looking forward to Confirmation at a later date.

THE GIFTS OF THE HOLY SPIRIT

After his first Reconciliation Freddie Freckles realised that he had learnt a lot about new beginnings. He had explained to the priest everything that he was really sorry about and the priest had been very helpful, reminding him that once we are forgiven, we leave those problems behind and make a fresh start. Freddie felt happy and free and although he still got up to mischief sometimes, when he was in the wrong he was usually quick to say he was sorry, so that he could recapture that feeling of freedom and happiness.

In the next session of the programme, the catechists were teaching the children about the fact that all the sacraments they were receiving are providing opportunities for new beginnings. In fact they are called the "sacraments of Christian Initiation" and the word "initiation" simply means "beginning"!

The group was now going to think about Confirmation. The first link here is with the sacrament of Baptism, the very first sacrament the children had received; most of them, like Freddie, when they were little babies. At the Confirmation ceremony it would be really important for them to be ready to answer the same questions that their parents and godparents had answered for them at their Baptism all those years ago. Fr Tim had turned up at the session and told them that this would be the easiest exam they would ever have to take. Unlike other exams when they worried about getting the answers wrong, this time they couldn't go wrong. There was just one answer to all the questions and they would answer all together: I DO. "Okay," he said, "it may be easy to remember the answer, but the important thing is that you really mean the answer." Fr Tim went on to say, "So when the bishop or the priest asks you the questions, you are saying, 'Yes, I really do believe in God the Father who made me and wants the best for me. I really do believe in this God who sent the Holy Spirit to Mary so that Jesus, the Son of God, could be born into our world and teach me all about how much God loves me and wants me to be a loving person. I really do believe that the same Holy Spirit is going to come to me at Confirmation in a new and powerful way to fill me those wonderful gifts, which will make me a true friend of Jesus.'"

Freddie thought: wow, this is really going to be a new beginning for me. He thought back to the time when he had moved to a new home with his family, and what a challenge that had been. He and Suzie had to change schools and make new friends, and adapting to the new situation had not been easy. However, looking back, Freddie realised just how much he had grown up during that time. Here he was being asked to grow up spiritually – deep down inside himself and he was excited about it.

The big problem Freddie had was: how was he going to remember everything, especially the names of these gifts the Holy Spirit was going to give him? There were seven of them and most of them seemed to be big words. Now Freddie's mum had a wonderful memory and when she was a little girl she had learnt that the great way to remember things was to make connections, which would remind you what it was you were trying to remember. She had learnt the seven gifts of the Holy Spirit by doing just that. So Freddie's mum sat down with him and taught him how she had remembered the gifts of the Holy Spirit when she was preparing for Confirmation.

Firstly, Freddie's mum reminded him that although they might be big words the gifts of the Holy Spirit are real things that would happen to him and make a real difference to his life.

Wisdom: She told him to think of the wise men who came to visit Jesus when he was a little baby. Because they were wise, they had the gift of **wisdom** and their minds were open to learn the difference between good things and bad things. So they were always eager to learn and have **knowledge**. This is the second great gift of the Holy Spirit. Now she reminded Freddie that they didn't just want to know lots of things, the wise men also wanted to understand why things happened and the way things work. This is the third great gift of the Holy Spirit: **understanding**. So his mum told him to remember those three gifts together because they lead on from one another:

Wisdom
Knowledge
Understanding

Then she reminded Freddie that the wise men, using their wisdom, knowledge and understanding, had followed the sign of the star that had led them to visit the new-born Saviour. To be able to do this they had to make a judgement about the message to go and search for this special baby. This is the next of the great gifts: **judgement**. But having made the right judgement, they still needed the courage to follow the star and make the journey, for they will have known that it would be a long and difficult one. And there is the next gift: **courage**. So you now have the next two gifts, which follow from the first three:

Judgement

Courage

And finally Freddie's mum told him about the other great gifts. When the wise men finally arrived to see the baby Jesus, they were filled with awe and wonder: they were amazed. So what did they do? They bowed down and showed the baby reverence, giving him their presents. "So, Freddie," said his mum, "that's what Jesus wants you to do as you get ready for your Confirmation and first Holy Communion. He wants you to be full of **wonder** at God's amazing world and the fact that he wishes always to live inside you. That will make you full of **reverence** for holy things. You will remember to genuflect (go down on one knee) when you enter the church because Jesus is always there in Holy Communion in the tabernacle. You will also, I hope, have a new reverence for all your friends and indeed all people because they, like you, are children of God." So there you have the last two gifts:

Wonder (Awe)

Reverence

Freddie had got it. When he went to bed he thought of the gifts. He thought of the wise men and immediately he remembered the first three gifts, one leading to the other: **wisdom**, **knowledge** and **understanding**. Then he thought of the next two because of the journey they had to make. Firstly they had to make the right **judgement** and then they needed the **courage** to see it through. And finally when they reached Jesus in Bethlehem they were so filled with **wonder** they knelt down and gave him their gifts with great **reverence**.

Freddie woke up the next morning and he still had all the gifts firmly in his mind. At breakfast he said, "Mum, I have got them: the wise men help me to think of **wisdom**, **knowledge** and **understanding**. Their journey leads me to think of their **judgement** and **courage**. Their arrival in Bethlehem reminds me of their **wonder** and **reverence**."

"Cheers, Freddie," said his mum. "Now live like the wise men and everyone will know that you are a friend of Jesus, filled with the gifts of the Holy Spirit."

PRAYER

Prayer

The lesson

The purpose of this story is to help the children realise that prayer is not just about our efforts to speak to God, but that God is speaking to us and actually living inside us. Like the little seed in the pot of earth, God's Spirit has been planted inside us so that we can grow up to be strong and loving people. It is possible to introduce children to the whole idea of contemplative prayer by getting them to be still and think of themselves lying in God's arms, like a little baby, or breathing in the life of God, the Holy Spirit.

Scripture reference

> Jesus said, "When you pray, do not babble as the pagans do, for they think that by using many words they will make themselves heard... So you should pray like this: 'Our Father...'" (Matthew 6:7-9)

> When we cannot choose words in order to pray properly, the Spirit himself expresses our plea in a way that could never be put into words.
> (Romans 8:26)

> Jesus said, "Unless you change and become like little children you will never enter the kingdom of heaven." (Matthew 18:3)

When to tell this story

Although this story comes in the sequence of stories preparing children for the sacraments, it stands in its own right as a story to help children to pray at any time.

Notes

This story will have much more impact if time can be found to let the children experience a period of stillness and silence when they picture themselves in the arms of God as a loving parent.

PRAYER

After learning how to remember the gifts of the Holy Spirit in the last session, Freddie had been practising his memory skills ever since. He was always looking for connections when he wanted to memorise things and generally finding that it worked really well.

Freddie knew that the next session was about prayer. To be honest, he wasn't much looking forward to it because he usually found prayer quite difficult. Often his mind would wander off and think about other things when he was supposed to be praying. He used to try and he did say a prayer first thing in the morning and again before he went to bed. Freddie also tried when they were saying prayers in school or when he went to church. He had learnt the Our Father and the Hail Mary when he was very young, but what he found most helpful was talking to God in his own words. Before he went to bed he would say his Our Father and Hail Mary and a beautiful prayer his mum and dad had taught him about the angels watching over and protecting him all through the night. But then he would just talk to Jesus about the people who were on his mind. Sometimes it would be about someone who was ill, while at other times he would just say a big "thank you" for his family and friends – and he would try to remember to say "sorry" for the things he had done wrong or the people he had upset. From an early age his mum and dad had taught him to do this, saying that if he listened to St Paul's letters when they were read out in church, he would hear that St Paul was always praying for people by name and saying thanks for all their blessings, as well as trying to sort out their problems.

Freddie had also noticed how his mum and dad prayed. Sometimes he was fascinated at the way they would kneel in church with their eyes closed, completely still and seemingly in another world. For example, when his grandma was very ill he remembered that every day they would go into the church, light a candle and then spend a few minutes before Mary's statue and picture. One day Freddie asked his mum and dad what they said when they were praying like that. They explained that often they didn't say very much; they just remembered how Mary suffered with Jesus and then placed grandma in Jesus and Mary's loving care, asking that whatever happened they and grandma would always know that Jesus loved them and was with them. Later that day Freddie's dad took him aside and said, "Freddie that was a great question you asked us today. Do you remember when the apostles saw Jesus praying and they went over and asked him to teach them how to pray?" Freddie said, "Yes, I do, and he taught them to pray the Our Father." His dad then explained that the whole point of the Our Father was that it is not just a prayer to say, but a whole way of praying: it's the way all our prayers should be. He said: "We begin by showing God great reverence, saying that we know that he is our Father in heaven, that his name is holy and that we want his kingdom to spread everywhere with everyone doing what he wants, no matter how challenging that may be. And then we pray for all our needs: our daily bread, which includes our spiritual food, the Holy Communion you are preparing for, Freddie. We ask for forgiveness and pray that we may be forgiving people and then we ask for God's protection from all the bad things: evil and temptation." Freddie found his dad's explanation very helpful and when he prayed the Our Father afterwards he found it much easier to keep his mind on what he was saying, but that didn't mean that his mind didn't sometimes wander off.

Now, wonder of wonders, help was even at hand with this problem of Freddie's mind wandering. Fr Tim came into class one day and asked the boys and girls if any of them found prayer difficult or even boring at times. They all put up their hands, including Freddie. Then to their surprise Fr Tim said, "I understand, because so do I, but here is a little tip for you. You remember that last time we learnt about the gifts of the Holy Spirit? Well now, even St Paul admitted that at times he couldn't find the words to pray properly, so he reminded his friends - and I am reminding you - that they should never forget that the Spirit of God is living inside them. He told them that the Spirit of God would find words better than any words they could find for themselves and would speak to God our Father on their behalf. So children, I always begin my prayer just thinking of myself lying back in the arms of God the Father and letting the Spirit pray through me and for me. Just think of a tiny little baby in the arms of her mother. Every so often the little baby just opens her eyes to check that her mum is still there. You and I are the little baby: we just need to look up and check that God is there, loving us and looking after us - and God is!"

When Freddie went home he told his mum and dad and Suzie all about what Fr Tim had said. That night he thought of his best friend, Peter Pickles, and Peter's mum who had just given birth to a little baby; Freddie thought of the baby lying in Mrs Pickles' arms and looking up and giggling and gurgling. Before he went to bed that night Freddie said his usual prayers and then he just lay back, imagining himself as a little baby in God's arms: he looked up once or twice and said "thank you," and then fell asleep.

Early the next morning Freddie saw the little pot of earth he had been given during the last session of the sacramental programme. Everyone had been given a pot of earth and a little seed. They had planted the seed and been told to look after it and bring it back on the great day when they would be confirmed and receive Holy Communion. Guess what: Freddie looked at the pot and saw the first little shoot sprouting and he suddenly got the point of it all. The Holy Spirit was living inside him and, with those great gifts, would help him to grow bigger and stronger in every way. He was to be like the plant: he was to grow and flower and flourish so that people would know he was one of Jesus' friends.

That morning Freddie thought of God the Father holding him, he thought of God the Holy Spirit telling God the Father to bless him and all the people he loved and wanted to pray for. And finally he thought of Jesus, God the Son, as his friend, inviting him to his special supper when he would feed him with Holy Communion because he was now old enough and wise enough to understand the wonderful mystery. He understood that we are invited to be part of God's family and even share in God's special meal, the Mass.

THE MASS

The Mass

The lesson

The Mass is the source and summit of the Christian life and with Freddie and friends getting close to the time when they will receive their first Holy Communion, the story is designed to help the children place the Mass in its historical context and understand that in this celebration above all Jesus is fulfilling his promise of always being with us.

Scripture references

As they were eating Jesus took some bread, and when he had said the blessing he broke it and gave it to them. "Take it," he said, "this is my body." Then he took a cup, and when he had returned thanks he gave it to them, and all drank from it, and he said to them, "This is my blood, the blood of the covenant, which is to be poured out for many. I tell you solemnly, I shall not drink any more wine until the day I drink the new wine in the kingdom of God." (Mark 14:22-25)

In the Acts of the Apostles we hear how the early Christians simply met in one another's houses for Mass:

They went as a body to the Temple every day but met in their houses for the breaking of bread; they shared their food gladly and generously; they praised God and were looked up to by everyone. (Acts: 2:46-47)

When to tell this story

The story is designed to help children understand the different parts of the Mass and inculcate a sense of deep reverence. It also opens them up to the importance of all that happened in Holy Week. While the context is once again a preparation programme for Holy Communion, the story could be adapted and told at any time to help children enter more deeply into the mystery of the Eucharist.

Notes

Even when a priest is not available to actually celebrate Mass, parents or catechists could gather the children either in church or a suitable place and re-enact the story.

THE MASS

It was the season of Lent and Freddie was trying very hard to make sacrifices and be more generous. He knew that this was a special time when we remember that Jesus spent forty days in the desert and that it was leading up to Easter and the most important week in the Church's year, Holy Week. During that week we have Holy Thursday, the day Jesus had his last meal with the disciples, the Last Supper, followed by Good Friday, the day Jesus died on the cross. And then most important of all comes Easter Sunday, the day Jesus rose from the dead. The three days leading up to Easter are called the "Easter Triduum" and there are special services on each day. Freddie had learnt that at the Last Supper Jesus had spent a long time talking to his friends and promising them that although he would be going away, he would not leave them alone. Jesus promised to send the Holy Spirit, who would make it possible for him to stay with them even though he was also returning to his Father in heaven. And the great sign of him being with them would be when they did what he told them to do at the Last Supper, which is what we do at Mass.

Fr Tim had decided that because it was getting so close to their Confirmation and first Holy Communion, all the children in the group would have a special Mass with their parents and teachers just before the end of term and the Easter holidays. Freddie was really pleased because he was beginning to understand more and more and he never forgot how Fr Tim explained everything at that Mass.

When they were all settled in the church, Fr Tim began in the usual way, making the sign of the cross and greeting everyone by saying, "The Lord be with you". Then he asked them all to sit down and told them that like Jesus' friends, the disciples, they were being invited to have a meal with Jesus. Fr Tim said, "Think of it as being invited to Jesus' party. Now wouldn't it be dreadful if we were going to someone's party and we weren't speaking to one another because we had had a big quarrel. The first thing we would have to do is make friends again and this is why at the beginning of Mass we always ask Jesus to forgive us the things we have done wrong… so that nothing can spoil the party." The children and grown-ups all thought for a few moments about the things they were sorry for and then, after Fr Tim, they said, "Lord, have mercy," and he said the prayer of forgiveness.

Freddie was due to do the first reading: a couple of sentences from the Acts of the Apostles explaining how they used to celebrate Mass two thousand years ago. Before Freddie was called up, however, Fr Tim surprised everyone by saying that he wanted them to imagine that they were not celebrating Mass in a big church but in Freddie Freckles' home. He told them that after Jesus had gone back to heaven and long before there were lots and lots of Christians all over the world, they just used to meet in one another's houses and remember what Jesus had done at the Last Supper. Fr Tim explained that like the children now, when everyone was settled and they had forgiven each other for any upsets, they would remind themselves of all Jesus wanted them to do by listening to some readings from the scriptures. Freddie read his reading and then Fr Tim read from the Gospel where Jesus was talking to the disciples at the Last Supper and telling them that other people would know they were his friends by the love they showed to one another. Fr Tim then talked about all the wonderful things that were going to happen to the children in the next few weeks and how the Holy Spirit would come down and make Jesus present for them in Holy Communion and in the sacrament of Confirmation. He explained that the great sign of this was the laying on of hands, which happens in nearly all the sacraments and would happen for them at their Confirmation. But he told the children to watch him carefully because in a few moments he would be laying his hands over the bread and wine and praying that the Holy Spirit would come down on them so that Jesus would be there in Holy Communion.

Some of the children now brought the bread and wine to Fr Tim. They also brought lots of other things as well, like worksheets and footballs and medals – symbols of their work and recreation. Fr Tim reminded them that when they go to someone's party they would always take a gift and their gift to Jesus today was the whole of their lives, and above all their hearts of love. Fr Tim prepared the gifts on the altar and after the children had sung the "Holy, holy" they knelt down and watched and listened carefully. Fr Tim laid his hands over the gifts just as he said he would and then he said the words of Jesus at the Last Supper: "This is my body, this is my blood". Then he offered those gifts to God the Father, praying for everyone, including the Pope and the Bishop, all the people who were alive and all the people who had died.

Now the children stood up because they were going to pray the Our Father, the prayer Jesus had taught them. When the time came to give Holy Communion, Fr Tim reminded the children that in a few weeks they would be coming up to receive this precious gift of Jesus himself for the first time. He reminded them that at Jesus' party this was the food they would share and that sometimes it is described as the "food of angels". Today the children all came up with joined hands and Fr Tim prayed a beautiful prayer over them, asking that our Lord would fill them with his life and love. They noticed how reverently all the grown-ups came up to receive Holy Communion, making a special throne with their hands.

The ministers of Communion helped Fr Tim to wash the chalices and patens – the cups and dishes which they had used – and then Fr Tim asked everyone to stand up for the final prayer and blessing. He thanked the children for being so attentive and prayerful. Fr Tim said he could see they were ready to be confirmed and receive their first Holy Communion. He reminded them they had already sung lots of lovely hymns and songs – "We always sing well at parties, don't we?" he said – and now he invited them to sing their hearts out for the final song. They had sung their Gathering Song at the beginning of the Mass, but now they were going to sing their Go Forth song, a reminder that Jesus sends us out from Mass to spread his love and peace wherever we go.

Freddie and all his friends left the church that day feeling on top of the world. Now they realised just how close they were to the great day when they would receive their Confirmation and Holy Communion. Freddie's mum had been at the Mass and that evening they talked all about it at teatime. Holy Week was coming up and his mum and dad promised Freddie that they would go to the special Mass on the evening of Holy Thursday which recalls Jesus having the Last Supper with the disciples. They also promised him that they would go to church each day of the Triduum. It was going to be a very special Easter holiday this year.

THE STATIONS OF
THE CROSS

The Stations of the Cross

The lesson
The story is written to introduce the children to the ancient devotion of praying with Jesus as he made his way through the streets of the Jerusalem to Calvary, where he died for us. It will help to explain why all Catholic churches have the Stations of the Cross on their walls.

Scripture reference
The Passion narratives in Matthew, Mark, Luke and John's Gospels.

Seeing his mother and the disciple he loved standing near her, Jesus said to his mother, "Woman, this is your son." Then to the disciple he said, "This is your mother." And from that moment the disciple made a place for her in his home. (John 19:26-27)

The importance of the resurrection:

If Christ has not been raised then our preaching is useless and your believing it is useless… if Christ has not been raised, you are still in your sins. (1 Corinthians 15:14,17)

When to tell this story
This story would be especially suitable for telling any group of children during Lent and Holy Week, but could be used at any time to teach them that Jesus literally loved us to death. At the same time it is important to stress that nothing else will make sense if he had not risen on Easter Sunday.

THE STATIONS OF THE CROSS

Lent had begun and Freddie always found this a difficult time because he knew he was supposed to be making sacrifices and giving up things. This year Fr Tim had begun the special service on Ash Wednesday by telling the children not to see Lent as a miserable time, but an opportunity. He said that St Paul had compared being a friend of Jesus with being like an athlete, who has to go into strict training. Athletes and sportsmen and women have to make lots of sacrifices so that they can be fit and well and achieve their goals. Fr Tim said to everybody, teachers and children, "Let's start this Lent determined to keep a big smile on our faces, not least because Jesus told us that we shouldn't show off about making sacrifices by putting on gloomy looks."

Fr Tim reminded the children that Lent is a time to prepare for Easter, but that leading up to Easter we have Holy Week, when we think of

Jesus' sufferings and death. Lent lasts for forty days because Jesus spent that amount of time in the wilderness, preparing for his special work of spreading the news of God's kingdom. "Right," said Fr Tim, "this Lent, we are all going to set ourselves some positive goals. If we give things up, it will be so that we learn to have the courage to say 'no' to things that are not good for us or that we shouldn't be doing. But more than that, if we give things up and save some money we can put it towards our special Lenten charity, which once again will be our twinned school in Africa. Just think how successful our Christmas effort was and how happy the children were because of their wonderful Christmas." The last point that Fr Tim made was regarding doing things. He had suggested that just as Jesus spent a lot of time talking to his Father while he was in the desert, so we would do well to try and find some extra time for prayer, the kind of prayer that helps us understand that Jesus is very close to us and literally loves us to death.

Freddie didn't quite understand what Fr Tim meant. He was to understand better later in Lent when the children, as part of their preparation for the sacraments, began to get ready for their "Easter Special". The catechists told them that they were going to re-enact the Stations of the Cross in church on Good Friday and that their service would be open to the whole parish. In the event, many people came to share the occasion and, as with the Christmas Special, they were amazed at how good it was. "The Stations of the Cross" is an ancient devotion in the life of the Church, retracing the steps of Jesus through the streets of Jerusalem to the place where he was put to death, Calvary. If you go to Jerusalem you can walk the half mile or so from the place where Pilate would have condemned Jesus to the place where he was crucified. Christian pilgrims to the Holy Land always make this journey, but so that everyone can make the same journey in their minds and hearts, around all our churches we have fourteen stations (stopping places) to help us think about that journey of Jesus.

All the children were going to take part in the Easter Special, just as they had at Christmas. This time Freddie was chosen to be the main reader because he had a good clear voice and had learnt to use the microphone in the church.

As there were so many people taking part it was decided to re-enact the Stations of the Cross on the sanctuary, the holy place where the altar stood, rather than all around the church. The number of Stations was reduced, so that special emphasis could be given to the most important ones. Freddie read clearly and began by reminding everyone of how Pontius Pilate, even though he didn't really want to, sent Jesus to be crucified and made him carry his cross. Pilate was too much of a coward to stand up to the crowd. So we must always pray for the courage to do what is right. There are three Stations which tell us that Jesus fell down under the weight of the heavy cross, but the children just thought about Jesus falling once. Freddie reminded everyone that, in spite of all the pain he was suffering, Jesus never gave in: he got up after he had fallen and struggled on. This is a reminder to us that no matter how many struggles we have or sins we commit, we keep going, trying to do what God wants.

There are four Stations when we are told that Jesus met people: his mother; Simon from Cyrene, who was forced to help him carry his cross; Veronica who lovingly wiped his face with a cloth; and lots of the women from the city who were weeping for him. As each of these people met Jesus, Freddie explained how Jesus reached out and blessed them. When he was dying on the cross, Jesus gave his mother into the care of John and John into the care of his mother. We believe that St John was representing all of us at that moment, which is how we know that Jesus gave Mary to be the spiritual mother of all his children. Simon may have been forced to help Jesus, but we know that God will have blessed him as God blesses all of us when we help people who are in trouble. There is nothing in the scriptures about Veronica, but she also represents all those who reach out to look after people in trouble. We believe that the towel she used was left with an image of Jesus' face on it. The image of Jesus is imprinted on us whenever we are kind to one another. Jesus told the women from the city not to cry any more but to pray for themselves and their children. The message is loud and clear: we are to keep praying for all we need to be faithful friends of Jesus.

The final Stations are the saddest of all. Jesus has his clothes torn off and is then nailed to a cross, where he dies, hanging between two criminals. One of the criminals turns and asks Jesus to remember him when he comes into his kingdom. Jesus promises him that he will be in heaven that night. What a reminder: that no matter how much trouble we might get into, if we are sorry, God is always ready to forgive us.

The last two Stations remind us that Jesus was taken down from the cross and placed in his mother's arms – there are lots of famous paintings of this moment and a wonderful marble carving called the "Pietà" in St Peter's, Rome – and then Joseph of Arimathea and Nicodemus arranged to place his body in the tomb.

There was one last Station of the Cross, which is not one of the traditional fourteen, but which people sometimes add these days. The fifteenth Station is the Resurrection of Jesus from the dead. Freddie had a special message for this Station, which was the result of a discussion in class with Fr Tim when they had been talking about Holy Week and all the events they would be thinking about in the build up to Easter. Angela, one Freddie's friends, had put her hand up and asked Fr Tim, "Father, why do we call it 'Good Friday', when it was such a bad Friday?" Fr Tim had thought that this was a fantastic question and he agreed with Angela that it was a truly bad Friday. However, he told her that the only thing which made it a Good Friday was what happened on Easter Sunday. He reminded all the class that St Paul had told us that if Christ is not risen, then our sins have not been forgiven and our faith would be pointless.

Freddie had got it: he saw the reason why we are always making the sign of the cross. It is because Jesus literally loved us to death. It is because Jesus had conquered sin and suffering and death and gone to heaven to prepare a place for all of us. So the cross becomes a triumph and we even have a feast to celebrate this called "The Exaltation of the Holy Cross". Freddie read this message out, including the reference to Angela's question in class, and the Easter Special ended with everyone looking forward to Easter Sunday and wishing one another "A Happy Easter"!

MARY: THE FIRST DISCIPLE

Mary: The First Disciple

The lesson
As we learnt when Jesus was dying on the cross, Mary was given to us
to be our mother, but she is also the perfect example of what it means
to be a follower – a disciple – of her son, Jesus. The story notes some
of the key moments in the scriptures when Mary is present, including
being with the disciples when the Holy Spirit came at Pentecost.

Scripture references
The annunciation:
> *Hail Mary, full of grace, the Lord is with you.* (Luke 1:28)

The visitation:
> *Blessed are you among women, and blessed is the fruit of your womb.*
> (Luke 1:42)

The marriage feast at Cana:
> *His mother said to the servants, "Do whatever he tells you."*
> (John 2:5)

After the ascension we are told:
> *They went back to Jerusalem… and when they reached the city they
> went to the upper room where they were staying; (the apostles are
> named). All these joined in continuous prayer, together with several
> women, including Mary the mother of Jesus.* (Acts 1:12-14)

When to tell this story
This story has been written as a prelude to the sacrament of
Confirmation to help the children have that sense of discipleship
which comes from belonging to the family of the Church. However,
it could easily be used outside that context as a story to help children
understand the place of Mary and to introduce them to the rosary.

MARY: THE FIRST DISCIPLE

This was the last main session before the actual Mass of Confirmation and first Holy Communion: the last time the children and their parents would come together and work together with the catechists. Freddie remembered how his mum and dad had been a little bit anxious before the programme began, wondering how it would all work, but they had enjoyed it as much as Freddie - and that was true of all the children and their parents.

You will remember that it was Freddie's mum who had helped him to remember the seven gifts of the Holy Spirit by teaching him to make connections and after this last session on Mary, she sprang into action again. When they got home she said, "Come on, Freddie, let's have a look at all the things we covered today and see how we can remember them. I must admit I learnt a lot myself which I never knew before." Freddie's dad and Suzie said they would like to join in, so the whole family sat down over a cup of tea and began to talk.

To begin with, Freddie's mum admitted that she had never thought of Mary as a disciple of Jesus as well as being his mother, but now she could see how it all made sense. She said: "Do you remember, Freddie, when you were asked to present the new Archbishop with a gift when he visited the school and you said you would be too nervous? But your head teacher, Mr James, took you aside and reassured you, saying everyone would be there to support you and there was really nothing to worry about. Then you said you would do it and you were really pleased afterwards. Well, imagine how nervous Mary must have been when God's messenger, the Archangel Gabriel, came at the annunciation and asked her to be the mother of God's Son, Jesus. However, the angel reassured her that the Holy Spirit would come to her and everything would be all right, and of course Mary had the courage to say 'yes'."

Freddie's mum began to tell him how she pictured Mary as this beautiful, gentle young girl, who was so caring and thoughtful. She reminded Freddie that Gabriel had told Mary about her cousin, Elizabeth, who was going to be the mother of John the Baptist, and immediately Mary went on a long journey to visit her: the visitation. This reminded Freddie of Sarah, his cousin, who was expecting a baby and how he and the family had travelled a long way to visit and congratulate her as soon as they heard the news. The difference in Elizabeth's case was that she was an older woman and the news of her baby was unexpected. However, just as the Holy Spirit was God's gift to Mary when Gabriel came to her, so the Holy Spirit filled Elizabeth with joy at Mary's visit and she realised what a very special baby Mary was carrying in her womb.

Now Freddie's mum realised a connection she had never noticed before and said to Freddie: "Do you realise that the words of the Archangel Gabriel and then the words of Elizabeth are the first part of the Hail

Mary? Gabriel said: 'Hail Mary, full of grace, the Lord is with thee,' and Elizabeth said: 'Blessed art thou among women and blessed is the fruit of thy womb.'" Freddie was delighted with all this because he knew his grandma was buying him some rosary beads for the big day and that when you pray the rosary you say ten Hail Marys one after the other and think about all the different stories concerning Jesus. Freddie knew there were twenty different decades (sets of ten) and that the first two were the annunciation and the visitation. It was all beginning to make more sense.

This thought about the rosary beads led to a discussion about presents, and all the family joined in. Everyone agreed that they loved receiving presents, not just because they would enjoy the gifts themselves but because the gifts were signs of how much people loved them. Freddie knew he would receive lots of presents for his Confirmation and first Holy Communion, but his dad was quick to remind him that he was only receiving those gifts because he was going to receive the gifts of the Holy Spirit. His dad had been thinking this through as the discussion had been going on and he remembered lots of the other ideas the catechists had shared with them at that final session. Most importantly he remembered that Mary had been present at so many of the key moments in Jesus' life. She was the first one to encourage Jesus to begin his earthly work at the marriage feast of Cana when the young couple could have been embarrassed because they had run out of wine. Mary was there when Jesus died on the cross, unlike most of his close friends who had run away. And of course she was with the apostles in the upper room when the Holy Spirit came at Pentecost, the birthday of the Church.

With the help of his mum and dad Freddie was beginning to see more and more clearly the importance of making connections and how those connections help us to remember things. There was a lot to learn and he didn't have to worry about making all the connections all at once. Freddie could see that even his mum and dad had learnt a lot just by being with him during the different sessions over the past months. But now he was very clear in his mind that there were two great events which were going to become part of his life in a wholly new way at his Confirmation and first Holy Communion Mass. The first was the Last Supper, when Jesus gave us Holy Communion. The second was Pentecost, the event which happened fifty days after Jesus had risen from the dead, when the Holy Spirit came down on the apostles, and the Church, the family of Jesus, was born.

Pentecost was very dramatic. We are told that the apostles were startled by a powerful, noisy wind and then what seemed like tongues of fire came and rested on them. Previously they had been worried men, who feared that they might be killed the way Jesus had been killed; but now, filled with the Holy Spirit, they had lots of courage and new strength. The apostles left the upper room where they had been assembled and went out and freely spoke about Jesus, his resurrection and his love for everyone, telling the people to repent and believe in him.

At the end of that last session Fr Tim had come into the room and told the children that he would have one final meeting with them before their Mass of Confirmation and first Holy Communion. At that session they would try to imagine themselves with Jesus in the upper room at the Last Supper. Freddie and his pals thought this sounded like a really good idea, especially as they would be having some biscuits and juice to remind them of the bread and wine.

Finally, Fr Tim encouraged them to remember that Mary was their spiritual mother and was always praying for them and with them. He reminded them that when Jesus was dying on the cross, St John had been told that Mary was now his mother too and that at that moment

John was representing all of us who are Jesus' friends. Fr Tim said, "Remember that Mary was in the upper room with the apostles when the Holy Spirit came at Pentecost. She will be with you at your Confirmation. She will help you to be a good disciple of Jesus all through your life. Say the Hail Mary; pray to her every day."

THE UPPER ROOM

The Upper Room

The lesson
The purpose of this story is to help children see the connections between what happened for the disciples of Jesus and how Jesus does the same for us through the sacraments. There is a special focus on how, with the laying on of hands, the Holy Spirit makes Jesus present in all the sacraments. In this way we can take part in the great events that took place in the upper room in Jerusalem.

Scripture references
The description of the Last Supper in St John's Gospel: chapters 13 to 17. Note especially the washing of the disciples' feet (13:1-15) and Jesus' promise that he will not leave them orphans (14:17).
The Pentecost story: Acts 2:1-13.

When to tell this story
This story provides an ideal backdrop for the celebration of the sacraments of Confirmation and first Holy Communion. With a little adaptation it could be used on other occasions to help the children understand why it is important to participate in the celebration of the Eucharist.

Notes
This story will have maximum effect if the children are engaged in a dialogue over the different feelings of the disciples, beginning with the Last Supper, moving through the death and resurrection of Jesus and culminating with the coming of the Holy Spirit at Pentecost.

THE UPPER ROOM

The time was drawing near and all the children were getting more and more excited about their Mass of Confirmation and first Holy Communion. As well as popping into the special sessions in the parish centre, Fr Tim occasionally turned up at school to tell the children a story. He also tried to help them by answering any questions they wanted to ask. Now, with the teachers, he had planned a very special get-together in the school so that he could prepare them for the day itself. There were a few children in the group who didn't go to Freddie's school and so arrangements were made with their parents and their schools for them to come to Freddie's school that afternoon.

The children were taken out of their classroom and down to a special meeting room in the school. They noticed that everything had been beautifully prepared for them. Some tables had been put in a semi-circle and covered with white cloths and there were chairs for all the children and Fr Tim. Fr Tim sat in the centre and then showed them a beautiful painting of the Last Supper: the occasion when Jesus gathered his disciples for one last meal, the night before he was going to suffer and die. Fr Tim said, "Children, I want you to sit quietly for a moment and imagine that you are in that upper room in Jerusalem with Jesus. Just as I do at Mass, I am going to take the part of Jesus and all of you are going to be his disciples." Then he invited the children to join in the conversation.

First of all Fr Tim asked the children what sort of mood they imagined the disciples were in and why. Their hands were shooting up and they all agreed that in spite of the fact they had come together to celebrate a special feast – the Jewish Feast of the Passover - it was likely that the disciples were nervous and sad, knowing that there were people who were waiting to arrest Jesus and take him away. They talked about how Jesus had washed the feet of the disciples, noting that in those days this was a great act of hospitality because they may well have been walking on dusty roads and this would have freshened them up and made them feel good all over. They remembered that Peter had wanted to wash Jesus' feet instead, but Jesus explained to him that he was showing them how he wanted them to look after everyone when he was gone.

Then they thought about how at the end of the meal, which would have included roast lamb, Jesus had blessed the bread and wine, saying, "This is my body, this is my blood," before asking them to do the same thing in memory of him. Fr Tim reminded the children that Christians had been faithful to Jesus' command for the last two thousand years and this is why we celebrate Mass: it is doing what Jesus told us to do, knowing that he is keeping his promise to stay with us and fill us with his life.

Fr Tim now explained that during that Last Supper Jesus and the disciples had had a long conversation. In St John's Gospel it lasts for five chapters. Over and over again Jesus was trying to reassure the disciples that although he was going to be arrested and put to death the next day, he would not leave them like orphans: he would send the

Holy Spirit to help them to understand everything. In fact the Holy Spirit would make it possible for Jesus to remain not just by their side, but live inside them, so that they would remain united with him and with God the Father. He also told them that he was going to heaven to prepare a place for them and they knew the way to get there. Thomas told Jesus he didn't know the way, so Jesus gently reminded him that he was the way, which was why he was showing them how to live: taking care of everyone and doing the things he was doing, taking the bread and wine and praying to the Father. Then Philip asked to see the Father, and again Jesus had to remind him that he and the Father were totally united, so to see him was to see the Father.

Next Fr Tim wondered how much the children knew about the upper room. A few hands went up and some of the children were quick to remember that the disciples were also there on Easter Sunday night when Jesus returned, having left the tomb where he had been buried. That evening Jesus prayed that they would receive the Holy Spirit and filled them with his peace. "Can you think of another time when the disciples were in the upper room?" asked Fr Tim. Again lots of the children remembered that it was on Pentecost Day, the day when the Holy Spirit came so dramatically. Jesus had returned to his Father at the ascension, forty days after Easter. It was then that the disciples together with Mary and some more friends of Jesus went back to the upper room and waited for the coming of the Spirit. Now the children's hands were shooting up to tell Fr Tim that there had been a great wind, which reminded them that the Spirit is the breath of God, filling them with God's life, and then what seemed like tongues of fire settled on them. The disciples became all fired up and ready for action, filled with new courage and determination and all those gifts the Spirit brings.

Fr Tim smiled at the children and reassured them that at their Confirmation their hair wouldn't catch fire! He reminded them that in most of the sacraments there is a sign that the Holy Spirit is coming to us. Fr Tim had told them about this sign, which was that of the laying on of hands. He explained that when he goes to people who are sick he lays hands on them, praying that the Holy Spirit will come and comfort them. Likewise in the sacrament of Reconciliation the priest lays his hand out over the person, praying that the Holy Spirit will bring the forgiveness of God. When a priest or a bishop is ordained, the bishop lays hands on the person so that he may minister God's love to the people. Fr Tim said, "Watch me at Mass: just before I say the words 'This my body, this is my blood', I lay my hands over the bread and wine, praying that the Holy Spirit will come and make Jesus present. Now on your Confirmation day, you will receive the laying on of hands, so that like the disciples, you will be ready to do God's work for the rest of your lives. So when the moment comes for you, I want you to pray like mad that the Holy Spirit will fill you with all those wonderful gifts."

They did a quick check and everyone could remember the seven gifts of the Holy Spirit by thinking of the wise men. They thought of what made them wise and how they were then able to make the right decisions and have the courage to carry them out, leading them to Jesus, whom they reverenced as they looked at him in wonder. Wisdom, Knowledge, Understanding, Judgement, Courage, Wonder and Reverence…

Now, to remind the children of how Jesus and the disciples shared at the Last Supper, everyone had some juice and biscuits. Fr Tim ended by reminding them that in a few days they would be celebrating for real. They would receive the gifts of the Holy Spirit and Jesus in Holy Communion.

When the great day came, Freddie and all the children remembered that wonderful half hour when they had imagined they were in the upper room. Freddie did indeed pray like mad when he received the laying on of hands and he received Holy Communion with great reverence, making a throne of his hands. He could never before remember feeling so happy and so peaceful.